The KL Book

by Lynn Maslen Kertell
pictures by Sue Hendra and John R. Maslen

Scholastic Inc.
New York • Toronto • London • Auckland • Sydney • Mexico City • New Delhi • Hong Kong • Buenos Aires

Kangaroos

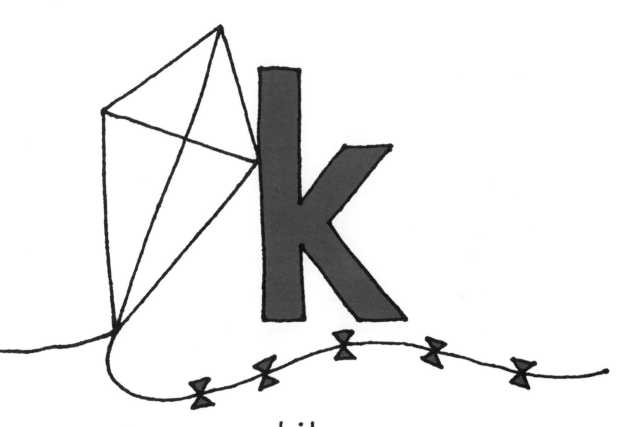

kite

Oops! Kangaroo finds a kitten

when she goes to kiss her kid.

Lunch box

lemons

Lion does not like finding

lemons in his lunch box.

"Let's make lemonade,"

says the kind kitten.

Look for these **k** and **l** words in this book.

kangaroo(s)   lemonade
kid   lemons
kind   let's
kiss   like
kite   lion
kitten   lunch box

Look for these additional **k** and **l** words in the pictures: kite string, koala bears, lamb, lettuce, and lizard.